LYRIC POETRY

Robert Pierce
Peter Neumeyer

James Moffett, Senior Editor

Houghton Mifflin Company · Boston

Atlanta   Dallas   Geneva, Ill.   Hopewell, N. J.   Palo Alto

Acknowledgments: "The Truth Is Quite Messy" by William Harris, from *Nine Black Poets* (1968). Reprinted by permission of Moore Publishing Company, Durham, N. C.

"Joy" is reprinted by permission of Charles Scribner's Sons from *Words* by Robert Creeley. Copyright © 1962, 1963, 1964, 1967 by Robert Creeley.

"Water Picture," which first appeared in *The New Yorker* (copyright © 1956 May Swenson) is reprinted by permission of Charles Scribner's Sons from *To Mix with Time* by May Swenson.

"Reuben Bright" is reprinted by permission of Charles Scribner's Sons from *Children of the Night* by Edwin Arlington Robinson (1897).

"Wind Song," from *Smoke and Steel* by Carl Sandburg. Copyright 1920 by Harcourt Brace Jovanovich, Inc.; renewed, 1948 by Carl Sandburg. Reprinted by permission of the publishers.

"Juggler," copyright 1949 by Richard Wilbur. Reprinted from his volume *Ceremony and Other Poems* by permission of Harcourt Brace Jovanovich, Inc. First published in *The New Yorker*.

"Do-It-Yourself Night" and "Dog Bone Blues," reprinted from *The Massachusetts Review,* copyright © 1963 by The Massachusetts Review Inc.

"It all started yesterday evening," from *The Liverpool Scene,* edited by Edward Lucie-Smith. Copyright © 1967 by Edward Lucie-Smith. Reprinted by permission of Doubleday & Company, Inc.

"January," from *Song at the Year's End* by R. S. Thomas. Reprinted by permission of Granada Publishing Limited.

"Silence" by Eugene Gomringer, reprinted by permission of London Magazine Limited.

"She Loves Me" by Emmett Williams, reprinted from *Anthology of Concretism,* edited by Eugene Wildman, copyright © 1969, by permission of The Swallow Press, Chicago.

"Football," text reprinted from *Walt Mason, His Book* by Barse Hopkins. Copyright 1916 by Barse Hopkins. Published by Grosset & Dunlap, Inc.

"Was a Man," from *The Islanders* by Philip Booth. Copyright © 1958 by Philip Booth. Reprinted by permission of The Viking Press.

"Nothing Is," copyright © 1968 by Sun Ra. Reprinted from *Black Fire,* edited by Larry Neal and LeRoi Jones, by permission of William Morrow & Co., Inc. and Ronald Hobbs Literary Agency.

"After the Dentist," reprinted by permission of Charles Scribner's Sons from *Half Sun Half Sleep.* Copyright © 1967 by May Swenson.

". . . Nor do I expect" by Kenneth Patchen. All Rights Reserved. Reprinted by permission of New Directions Publishing Corporation.

"My Old Cat," reprinted by permission of the author, Hal Summers.

"Ladies," from *Solitudes Crowded with Loneliness,* copyright © 1965 by Bob Kaufman. Reprinted by permission of New Directions Publishing Corporation.

"Critical Can Opener," from *Rommel Drives On Deep into Egypt* by Richard Brautigan. Copyright © 1970 by Richard Brautigan. A Seymour Lawrence Book/Delacorte Press. Reprinted by permission of the publisher.

Acknowledgments continued on page 135.

Contents

Next, see "Cinquains and Turn-Around Poems," "Contrast Poems," "Be a Song Writer," and "Comparison Poems" in MAKING THINGS UP; "Memories, Memories," "Feeling Poems," and "Moods" in PEOPLE; "Move to a Story," "Work Up a Reading," and "Language Moves" in ACTING OUT; and "What's Coming Up?" in WHAT DO YOU THINK?

○ For a recording of this selection, see *Lyric Poetry* in the LISTENING LIBRARY.

THE TRUTH
IS
QUITE MESSY

William J. Harris

Neatness, madam, has
nothing to do
with the Truth.
The Truth
is quite messy
like
a wind blown room.

JOY

Robert Creeley

I could look at
an empty hole for hours
thinking it will
get something in it,

will collect
things. There is
an infinite emptiness
placed there.

Upon
His
Departure
Hence

Robert Herrick

Thus I
Pass by
And die,

As one
Unknown
And gone.

I'm made
A shade
And laid

I' the grave;
There have
My cave.

Where tell
I dwell.
Farewell.

Water Picture

May Swenson

In the pond in the park
all things are doubled:
Long buildings hang and
wriggle gently. Chimneys
are bent legs bouncing
on clouds below. A flag
wags like a fishhook
down there in the sky.

The arched stone bridge
is an eye, with underlid
in the water. In its lens
dip crinkled heads with hats
that don't fall off. Dogs go by,
barking on their backs.
A baby, taken to feed the
ducks, dangles upside-down,
a pink balloon for a buoy.

Treetops deploy a haze of
cherry bloom for roots,
where birds coast belly-up
in the glass bowl of a hill;
from its bottom a bunch
of peanut-munching children
is suspended by their
sneakers, waveringly.

A swan, with twin necks
forming the figure three,
steers between two dimpled
towers doubled. Fondly
hissing, she kisses herself,
and all the scene is troubled:
water-windows splinter,
tree-limbs tangle, the bridge
folds like a fan.

REUBEN BRIGHT

Edwin Arlington Robinson

Because he was a butcher and thereby
Did earn an honest living (and did right)
I would not have you think that Reuben Bright
Was any more a brute than you or I;
For when they told him that his wife must die,
He stared at them, and shook with grief and fright,
And cried like a great baby half that night,
And made the women cry to see him cry.

And after she was dead, and he had paid
The singers and the sexton and the rest,
He packed a lot of things that she had made
Most mournfully away in an old chest
Of hers, and put some chopped-up cedar boughs
In with them, and tore down the slaughter-house.

Wind Song

Carl Sandburg

Long ago I learned how to sleep,
In an old apple orchard where the wind swept by counting
 its money and throwing it away,
In a wind-gaunt orchard where the limbs forked out and
 listened or never listened at all,
In a passel of trees where the branches
 trapped the wind into whistling, "Who, who are you?"
I slept with my head in an elbow on a summer afternoon
 and there I took a sleep lesson.
There I went away saying: I know why they sleep, I know
 how they trap the tricky winds.
Long ago I learned how to listen to the singing wind and
 how to forget and how to hear the deep whine,
Slapping and lapsing under the day blue and the night stars:
 Who, who are you?

 Who can ever forget
 listening to the wind go by
 counting its money
 and throwing it away?

A ball will bounce, but less and less. It's not
A light-hearted thing, resents its own resilience.
Falling is what it loves, and the earth falls
So in our hearts from brilliance,
Settles and is forgot.
It takes a sky-blue juggler with five red balls

JUGGLER

Richard Wilbur

To shake our gravity up. Whee, in the air
The balls roll round, wheel on his wheeling hands,
Learning the ways of lightness, alter to spheres
Grazing his finger ends,
Cling to their courses there,
Swinging a small heaven about his ears.

But a heaven is easier made of nothing at all
Than the earth regained, and still and sole within
The spin of worlds, with a gesture sure and noble
He reels that heaven in,
Landing it ball by ball,
And trades it all for a broom, a plate, a table.

Oh, on his toe the table is turning, the broom's
Balancing up on his nose, and the plate whirls
On the tip of the broom! Damn, what a show, we cry:
The boys stamp, and the girls
Shriek, and the drum booms
And all comes down, and he bows and says good-bye.

If the juggler is tired now, if the broom stands
In the dust again, if the table starts to drop
Through the daily dark again, and though the plate
Lies flat on the table top,
For him we batter our hands
Who has won for once over the world's weight.

Do-It-Yourself Night

Keith Gunderson

Just
take a
big space
growing
dark
and use   dot dot
mainly   and need
stars: even dot
dot dot   more
dot   dot dot
that's   to make
enough   dot dot
dot   the night
for dusk   dot
but we   complete
can't dot   dot dot
wait   dot dot
dot dot   dot dot
too long   well dot
dot dot   that dot
             does it
                 except
             thomp
             for a
             moon.

Dog Bone Blues

Keith Gunderson

what
a
bone
that
dog   now
got   and
I   bury
suppose it
he   later
will   or
bury   later
it   it
now   now
and   and
gnaw   bury
it   it
later   gnaw
or   or
gnaw   wow
it   what
         a
         bone
         that
         dog
         got.

It all started yesterday evening

Roger McGough

It all started yesterday evening
as i was helping the potatoes
off with their jackets
i heard you make a date
with the kettle
i distinctly
heard you making a date
with the kettle
my kettle

then at midnight
in the halflight
while i was polishing the bluespeckles
in a famous soap powder
i saw you fondling
the frying pan
i distinctly
saw you fondling the frying pan
my frying pan

finally at middawn
in the halflight
while waiting in the cool shadows
beneath the sink
i saw you making love
with the gas cooker
i distinctly
saw you making love
with the gas cooker
my gas cooker

my mistake was to leap upon
you crying:
'MONIKA SPARE THE SAUCERS'
for now you've left me
for someone
with a bigger kitchen

JANUARY

R. S. Thomas

The fox drags its wounded belly
Over the snow, the crimson seeds
Of blood burst with a mild explosion,
Soft as excrement, bold as roses.

Over the snow that feels no pity,
Whose white hands can give no healing,
The fox drags its wounded belly.

Silence

Eugene Gomringer

```
silence silence silence
silence silence silence
silence        silence
silence silence silence
silence silence silence
```

she loves me
she loves me not
she loves
she loves me
she
she loves
she

She Loves Me

Emmett Williams

Football

Walt Mason

The Game was ended, and the noise at last had died away, and now they gathered up the boys where they in pieces lay. And one was hammered in the ground by many a jolt and jar; some fragments never have been found, they flew away so far. They found a stack of tawny hair, some fourteen cubits high; it was the half-back, lying there, where he had crawled to die. They placed the pieces on a door, and from the crimson field, that hero then they gently bore, like soldier on his shield. The surgeon toiled the livelong night above the gory wreck; he got the ribs adjusted right, the wishbone and the neck. He soldered on the ears and toes, and got the spine in place, and fixed a guttapercha nose upon the mangled face. And then he washed his hands and said: "I'm glad that task is done!" The half-back raised his fractured head, and cried: "I call this fun!"

Was a Man

Philip Booth

Was a man, was a two-
faced man, pretended
he wasn't who he was,
who, in a men's room,
faced his hung-over
face in a mirror hung
over the towel rack.
The mirror was cracked.
Shaving close in that
looking glass, he nicked
his throat, bled blue
blood, grabbed a new
towel to patch the wrong
scratch, knocked off
the mirror and, facing
himself, almost intact,
in final terror hung
the wrong face back.

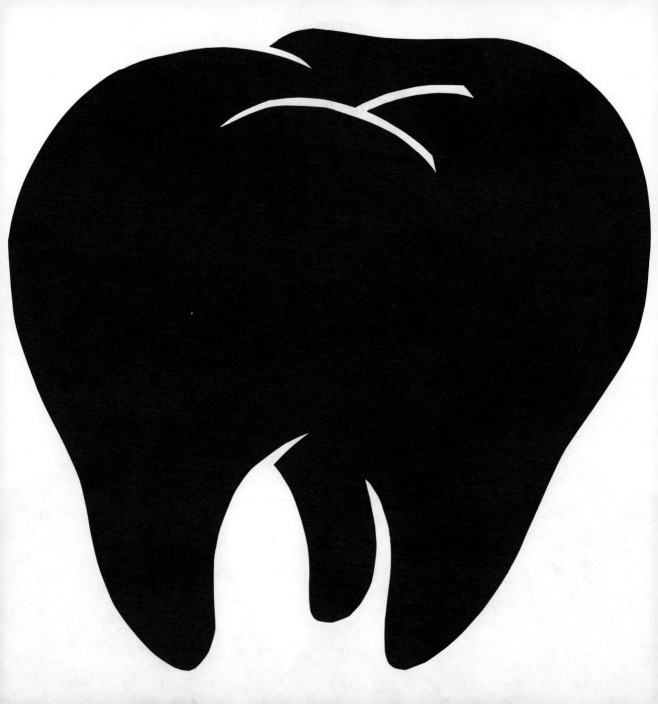

After
the
Dentist

May Swenson

My left upper
lip and half

my nose is gone.
I drink my coffee

on the right from
a warped cup

whose left lip dips.
My cigarette's

thick as a finger.
Somebody else's.

I put lip-
stick on a cloth-

stuffed doll's
face that's

surprised when one
side smiles.

Nothing Is

Sun Ra

At first nothing is;
Then nothing transforms itself to be air
Sometimes the air transforms itself to be water;
And the water becomes rain and falls to earth;
Then again, the air through friction becomes fire.
So the nothing and the air and the water
And the fire are really the same—
Upon different degrees.

... *Nor do I expect*

Kenneth Patchen

". . . nor do I expect
Fleece to grow on doorknobs—"

We were all sitting around
in the coffee shop
cutting each other—
having a nervous ball.
When an angel dropped in
and said, I swear, directly to me:
"There is no love among you."
"Hell, baby," I said,
"do you expect flowers
to grow on doorknobs?"

MY OLD CAT

Hal Summers

My old cat is dead,
Who would butt me with his head.
He had the sleekest fur.
He had the blackest purr.
Always gentle with us
Was this black puss,
But when I found him today
Stiff and cold where he lay
His look was a lion's,
Full of rage, defiance:
Oh, he would not pretend
That what came was a friend
But met it in pure hate.
Well died, my old cat.

LADIES

Bob Kaufman

How many ladies in how many paintings
Escaped how many snakes?

How many snakes in how many paintings
Escaped how many ladies?

Every lady escaped, but one.
Not one goddam snake ever escaped.

It's a hell of a lot safer
To be a lady
Than a snake.

Critical Can Opener

Richard Brautigan

There is something wrong
with this poem. Can you
    find it?

SEA LULLABY

Elinor Wylie

The old moon is tarnished
With smoke of the flood,
The dead leaves are varnished
With color like blood,

A treacherous smiler
With teeth white as milk,
A savage beguiler
In sheathings of silk,

The sea creeps to pillage,
She leaps on her prey;
A child of the village
Was murdered today.

She came up to meet him
In a smooth golden cloak,
She choked him and beat him
To death, for a joke.

Her bright locks were tangled,
She shouted for joy,
With one hand she strangled
A strong little boy.

Now in silence she lingers
Beside him all night
To wash her long fingers
In silvery light.

PICTURE # 16

Lawrence Ferlinghetti

Three maidens went over the land
One carried a piece of bread
                        in the hand
One said
          Let's divide it and cut it

And they strolled thru a red forest
and in the red forest
                    there stood a red church
and in the red church
                    stood a red altar
and upon the red altar
                    lay a red knife
and now we come to the parable
                              They
took the red knife and wounded
                          their bread
and where they cut with the
                        so red knife
                              it was red

The Sorrow of Kodio

Miriam Koshland

We were three women, three men
And myself, Kodio Ango.
We were on our way to work in the city
And I lost my wife, Nanama, on the way.
I alone have lost my wife,
To me alone such misery has happened,
To me alone, Kodio,
The most handsome of the three men,
Such misery has happened.
In vain I call for my wife.
She died on the way like a chicken running.
How shall I tell her mother?
How shall I tell it to her, I Kodio,
When it is so hard
To hold back my own pain?

GHOST DANCE SONGS

These songs were sung by Plains Indians as part of the Ghost Dance Religion. The songs were accompanied by dancing and induced in the participant a trance-like state, which was believed to make him impervious to harm and place him in harmony with the Great Spirit.

1

My children,
When at first I liked the whites,
I gave them fruits,
I gave them fruits.

2

Father have pity on me,
I am crying for thirst,
All is gone,
I have nothing to eat.

3

The father will descend,
The earth will tremble,
Everybody will arise,
Stretch out your hands.

4

The Crow — *Ehe'eye!*
I saw him when he flew down,
To the earth, to the earth.
He has renewed our life,
He has taken pity on us.

5

I circle around
The boundaries of the earth,
Wearing the long wing feathers,
As I fly.

6

I' yehé! my children —
My children,
We have rendered the desolate.
The whites are crazy — Ahé yuhé yu!

7

We shall live again,
We shall live again.

FEEDING THE LIONS

Norman Jordan

They come into
our neighborhood
with the sun
an army of
social workers
carrying briefcases
filled with lies
and stupid grins
Passing out relief
checks
and food stamps
hustling from one
apartment to another
so they can fill
their quota
and get back out
before dark.

the soul is a beautiful thing
& i live by the soul
when i walk
it takes me
        today
i didn't go to school
i read
got high
ate
read
wrote
got high
spoke to carlos
saw the indians
on t.v.
& in my mind
& heart
they kick
the white man
in the ass
went down
got high
took a bus
honeychild
& claudia

giggled
about paul
homemade
chicken
& rice
found a dime
sticking
in the tar
jefferson park
the wind
talks
night
morning
no school
black coffee
corn muffin
read david's
felix
listened
to joe battan
wrote
i learned
today
beautiful
soul
went down
spoke to some

children
& slowly
remembered

three days/out of Franklin

Victor Hernandez Cruz
(exiled from Franklin December 14 to 19)

chino
singing
baby
O
baby
in the
hallway
at 12–17
i smiled
at the rain
when it fell
from the window
wrote
head
night
morning
no school
but the world
& my soul
& all the love
that wants to
blow up
like joe bataan's
trombones
night

three days
with myself
& the world
soul is beautiful
thing
the smell of
everything
ahead
the earth
& all the people/

SNAKE

Theodore Roethke

I saw a young snake glide
Out of a mottled shade
And hang, limp on a stone:
A thin mouth, and a tongue
Stayed, in the still air.

It turned; it drew away;
Its shadow bent in half;
It quickened, and was gone.

I felt my slow blood warm.
I longed to be that thing,
The pure, sensuous form.
And I may be, some time.

Complete Destruction

William Carlos Williams

It was an icy day,
We buried the cat,
then took her box
and set match to it

in the back yard.
Those fleas that escaped
earth and fire
died by the cold.

EPITAPH

Malcolm Lowry

Malcolm Lowry
Late of the Bowery
His prose was flowery
And often glowery
He lived, nightly, and drank, daily,
And died playing the ukulele.

Suicide's Note

Langston Hughes

The calm,
Cool face of the river
Asked me for a kiss.

That Dark Other Mountain

Robert Francis

My father could go down a mountain faster than I
Though I was first one up.
Legs braced or with quick steps he slid
   the gravel slopes
Where I picked cautious footholds.

Black, Iron, Eagle, Doublehead, Chocorua,
Wildcat and Carter Dome—
He beat me down them all. And that last
   other mountain,
And that dark other mountain.

A Sound from the Earth

William Stafford

Somewhere, I think in Dakota,
they found the leg bones—just the
big leg bones—of several hundred
buffalo, in a gravel pit.

Near there, a hole in a cliff
has been hollowed so that
the prevailing wind
thrums a note so low and persistent
that bowls of water placed in that
cave will tremble to foam.

The grandfather of Crazy Horse
lived there, they say, at the last,
and his voice like the thrum of the hills
made winter come as he sang, "Boy,
where was your buffalo medicine?
I say you were not brave enough, Boy.
I say Crazy Horse was too cautious."

Then the sound he cried out for his grandson
made that thin Agency soup that they
put before him tremble. The whole
earthen bowl churned into foam.

Concrete Trap

Elizabeth Coatsworth

The fox at midnight in the city square
knows there's a way, but knows not which it is,
a path that leads to fields and woods and lair,
leaves underfoot, earth and the stirring air.
Bewildered stands the fox, too many streets
lead off too many ways, yet there is one
leads to the woods and to tomorrow's sun.
Under street lamps, between the straight house walls,
hard, geometric, baffling nose and eyes,
escape is there for him to recognize.
Bewildered stands the fox, questing the way,
and in the yards the dogs begin to bay.

INVOCATION

Helene Johnson

Let me be buried in the rain
In a deep, dripping wood,
Under the warm wet breast of Earth
Where once a gnarled tree stood.
And paint a picture on my tomb
With dirt and a piece of bough
Of a girl and a boy beneath a round, ripe moon
Eating of love with an eager spoon
And vowing an eager vow.
And do not keep my plot mowed smooth
And clean as a spinster's bed,
But let the weed, the flower, the tree,
Riotous, rampant, wild, and free,
Grow high above my head.

Therzacat Boogie

Keith Gunderson

cat-parts
cat-parts
hangun'
in the
dusk-dark,
hangun'
there
wearun'
glare
side by side,
but the
eye-holes
on the
body-place
make a
one thing . . .
yeaaaaaah . . .
the
eye-holes
on the
body-place
make a
one thing.

Christmas morning I
Got up before the others and
ran
Naked across the plank
Floor into the front
Room to see grandmama
Sewing a new
Button on my last year
Ragdoll.

Christmas Morning I

Carole Freeman

Night Clouds

Amy Lowell

The white mares of the moon rush along the sky
Beating their golden hoofs upon the glass Heavens;
The white mares of the moon are all standing on their hind legs
Pawing at the green porcelain doors of the remote Heavens.
Fly, mares!
Strain your utmost,
Scatter the milky dust of stars,
Or the tiger sun will leap upon you and destroy you
With one lick of his vermilion tongue.

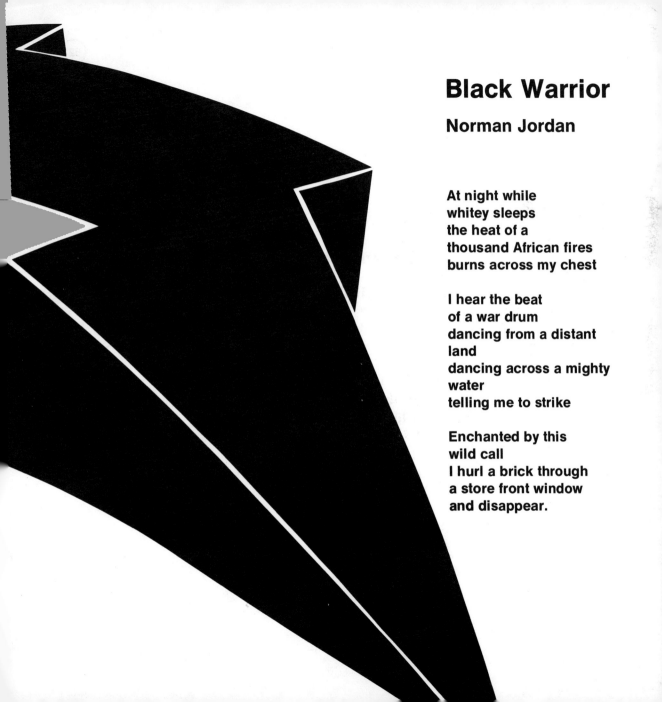

Black Warrior

Norman Jordan

At night while
whitey sleeps
the heat of a
thousand African fires
burns across my chest

I hear the beat
of a war drum
dancing from a distant
land
dancing across a mighty
water
telling me to strike

Enchanted by this
wild call
I hurl a brick through
a store front window
and disappear.

Upon Julia's Clothes

Robert Herrick

Whenas in silks my Julia goes
Then, then (methinks) how sweetly flows
That liquefaction of her clothes.

Next, when I cast mine eyes and see
That brave vibration each way free;
O how that glittering taketh me!

The Naming of Cats

T. S. Eliot

The Naming of Cats is a difficult matter,
　　It isn't just one of your holiday games;
You may think at first I'm as mad as a hatter
When I tell you, a cat must have THREE DIFFERENT NAMES.
First of all, there's the name that the family use daily,
　　Such as Peter, Augustus, Alonzo or James,
Such as Victor or Jonathan, George or Bill Bailey—
　　All of them sensible everyday names.
There are fancier names if you think they sound sweeter,
　　Some for the gentlemen, some for the dames:
Such as Plato, Admetus, Electra, Demeter—
　　But all of them sensible everyday names.
But I tell you, a cat needs a name that's particular,
　　A name that's peculiar, and more dignified,

Else how can he keep up his tail perpendicular,
  Or spread out his whiskers, or cherish his pride?
Of names of this kind, I can give you a quorum,
  Such as Munkustrap, Quaxo, or Coricopat,
Such as Bombalurina, or else Jellylorum—
  Names that never belong to more than one cat.
But above and beyond there's still one name left over,
  And that is the name that you never will guess;
The name that no human research can discover—
  But THE CAT HIMSELF KNOWS, and will never confess.
When you notice a cat in profound meditation,
  The reason, I tell you, is always the same:
His mind is engaged in a rapt contemplation
  Of the thought, of the thought, of the thought of his name:
    His ineffable effable
    Effanineffable
Deep and inscrutable singular Name.

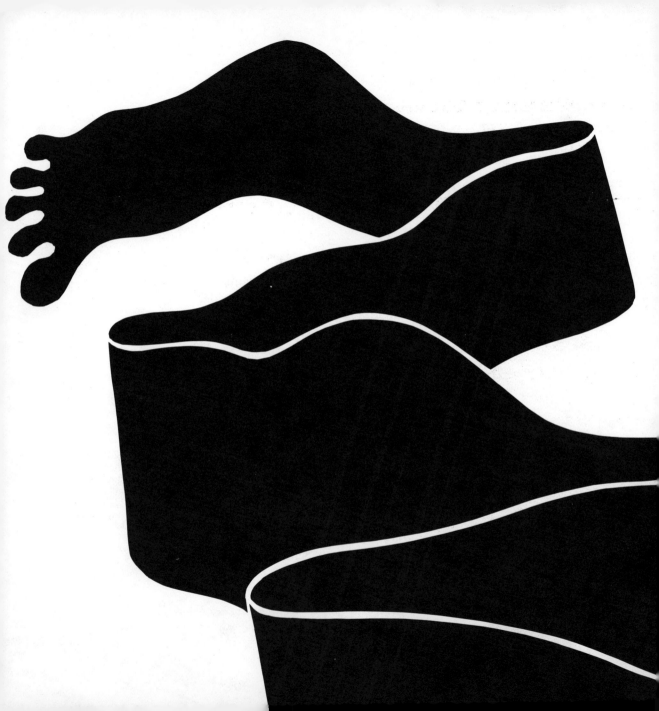

400-Meter Freestyle

Maxine W. Kumin

THE GUN full swing the swimmer catapults and cracks

    s

      i

        x

feet away onto that perfect glass he catches at

a

n

 d

throws behind him scoop after scoop cunningly moving

      t

        h

          e

water back to move him forward. Thrift is his wonderful

 s

  e

   c

ret; he has schooled out all extravagance. No muscle

       r

        i

         p

ples without compensation wrist cock to heel snap to

h
i
s
mobile mouth that siphons in the air that nurtures
                                                  h
                                                    i
                                                      m
at half an inch above sea level so to speak.
T
h
  e
astonishing whites of the soles of his feet rise
                                                a
                                                  n
                                                    d
salute us on the turns. He flips, converts, and is gone
a
l
l
in one. We watch him for signs. His arms are steady at
                                                      t
                                                        h
                                                          e
catch, his cadent feet tick in the stretch, they know
t
h
  e
lesson well. Lungs know, too; he does not list for
                                                  a
                                                    i
                                                      r

he   drives   along   on   little   sips   carefully   expended
b
u
t
that   plum   red   heart   pumps   hard   cries   hurt   how   soon
                                                                    i
                                                                      t
                                                                        s
near   one   more   and   makes   its   final   surge   TIME: 4:25:9

RACOON

Kenneth Rexroth

The racoon wears a black mask,
And he washes everything
Before he eats it. If you
Give him a cube of sugar,
He'll wash it away and weep.
Some of life's sweetest pleasures
Can be enjoyed only if
You don't mind a little dirt.
Here a false face won't help you.

Rest Stop

Donald Jones

Showing his friend
how he could shoot,
he nailed a bird
at three hundred feet.

How he could shoot
a mourning dove
on a high, taut wire
perched close to his love.

The mourning dove
at the crack of the shot
dropped in a clump
by the road to rot.

At the crack of the shot
his wife not far
asked what bird
he'd shot from the car.

His wife in the car,
his friend as a third,
he started and said,
"Oh, some small bird."

When I Was One-and-Twenty

A. E. Housman

WHEN I was one-and-twenty
  I heard a wise man say,
'Give crowns and pounds and guineas
  But not your heart away;
Give pearls away and rubies
  But keep your fancy free.'
But I was one-and-twenty,
  No use to talk to me.

When I was one-and-twenty
  I heard him say again,
'The heart out of the bosom
  Was never given in vain;
'Tis paid with sighs a plenty
  And sold for endless rue.'
And I am two-and-twenty,
  And oh, 'tis true, 'tis true.

Dark Girl

Arna Bontemps

Easy on your drums,
Easy wind and rain,
And softer on your horns,
She will not dance again.

Come easy little leaves
Without a ghost of sound
From the China trees
To the fallow ground.

Easy, easy drums
And sweet leaves overhead,
Easy wind and rain;
Your dancing girl is dead.

Romeo and Juliet

Richard Brautigan

If you will die for me,
I will die for you

and our graves will
be like two lovers washing
their clothes together
in a laundromat.

If you will bring the soap,
I will bring the bleach.

NIGHTMARE

Anne Mary

In a summer cottage
of hollyhocks,
my father killed
the marauding fox.
My supper milk spilled
when the shot rang out

and splintered my world
with doubt.

That thief took chickens
night after night
from the angry farmers
across the road;
yet memory sickens
me at the sight
of father's fingers
dripping red.

No matter how gently
they stroked my head,
that night I hid
my eyes.
Later I drowned
in a crimsom dream
until I woke up
with a chilling scream . . .
A fox had towered over a bed
with father in it—dead.

The Draft Horse

Robert Frost

With a lantern that wouldn't burn
In too frail a buggy we drove
Behind too heavy a horse
Through a pitch-dark limitless grove.

And a man came out of the trees
And took our horse by the head
And reaching back to his ribs
Deliberately stabbed him dead.

The ponderous beast went down
With a crack of a broken shaft.
And the night drew through the trees
In one long invidious draft.

The most unquestioning pair
That ever accepted fate
And the least disposed to ascribe
Any more than we had to to hate,

We assumed that the man himself
Or someone he had to obey
Wanted us to get down
And walk the rest of the way.

Apfel

Reinhard Döhl

pfelApfelApfelApfe
felApfelApfelApfelApfelA
felApfelApfelApfelApfelApfe
ApfelApfelApfelApfelApfelApf
pfelApfelApfelApfelApfelA
ApfelApfelApfelApfelApfelApfe
pfelApfelApfelApfelApfelA
ApfelApfelApfelApfelApfelApfe
felApfelApfelApfelApfelApfel
ApfelApfelApfelApfelApf
elApfelApfelApfelWurmAp
felApfelApfelApfelApfel
pfelApfelApfelApfel
pfelApfelApfelA
nfelApfelA

All day I hear

James Joyce

All day I hear the noise of waters
   Making moan,
Sad as the sea-bird is, when going
   Forth alone,
He hears the winds cry to the waters'
   Monotone.

The grey winds, the cold winds are blowing
   Where I go.
I hear the noise of many waters
   Far below.
All day, all night, I hear them flowing
   To and fro.

PRELUDE 1

T.S. Eliot

The winter evening settles down
With smell of steaks in passageways.
Six o'clock.
The burnt-out ends of smoky days.
And now a gusty shower wraps
The grimy scraps
Of withered leaves about your feet
And newspapers from vacant lots;
The showers beat
On broken blinds and chimney-pots,
And at the corner of the street
A lonely cab-horse steams and stamps.
And then the lighting of the lamps.

A Winter Song

William J. Harris

If I
were the
cold weather
and people
talked about me
the way they talk
about it,
I'd just
pack up
and leave town.

My Story

*(translated from the Gaelic
by Brendan Kennelly)*

Here's my story; the stag cries,
Winter snarls as summer dies.

The wind bullies the low sun
In poor light; the seas moan.

Shapeless bracken is turning red,
The wildgoose raises its desperate head.

Birds' wings freeze where fields are hoary.
The world is ice. That's my story.

DINKY

Theodore Roethke

O what's the weather in a Beard?
It's windy there, and rather weird,
And when you think the sky has cleared
  — Why, there is Dirty Dinky.

Suppose you walk out in a Storm,
With nothing on to keep you warm,
And then step barefoot on a Worm
  — Of course, it's Dirty Dinky.

As I was crossing a hot hot Plain,
I saw a sight that caused me pain,
You asked me before, I'll tell you again:
  — It *looked* like Dirty Dinky.

Last night you lay a-sleeping? No!
The room was thirty-five below;
The sheets and blankets turned to snow.
  — He'd got in: Dirty Dinky.

You'd better watch the things you do.
You'd better watch the things you do.
You're part of him; he's part of you
  — *You* may be Dirty Dinky.

SNOWSHOEING

John Caddy

I

Morning still and cold, the spruce
heavy with new snow. Breath is my only sound.
The first tracks I see are of mice and voles
delicate trails appearing from tunnels under the snow
faint lines of their tails between bird prints.
The tracks run five or six feet and dive back into holes,
the brief journeys into night sometimes visibly ended,
a subtle disturbance at the end of the track,
the mark of the owl. It is cold.
The day is silent as feathers.

II

Suddenly between my snowshoes
a partridge exploding from deep snow
loud drumming of wings
powder thrown into sunlight
I almost fall down then she's gone,
crystals sifting over me.
A moment after the only sign
a soft unshadowed hollow
where she sat out the storm
and on each side
the marks of her wingtips in snow.

III

Sky graying down.
Must be 20 below, and dropping.
I hear the first report of sap freezing in hardwood,
snapping like a shot. My breath
and bursting cells, sap turned to ice
shattering branches and trunks.
As the cold settles in, the brittle cracks
echo more frequently, the only sound,
except once
a raven's gutty caw.

War Is Kind

Stephen Crane

Do not weep, maiden, for war is kind.
Because your lover threw wild hands toward the sky
And the affrighted steed ran on alone,
Do not weep.
War is kind.

    Hoarse, booming drums of the regiment,
    Little souls who thirst for fight,
    These men were born to drill and die.
    The unexplained glory flies above them,
    Great is the battle-god, great, and his kingdom—
    A field where a thousand corpses lie.

Do not weep, babe, for war is kind.
Because your father tumbled in the yellow trenches,
Raged at his breast, gulped and died,
Do not weep.
War is kind.

    Swift blazing flag of the regiment,
    Eagle with crest of red and gold,
    These men were born to drill and die.
    Point for them the virtue of slaughter,
    Make plain to them the excellence of killing
    And a field where a thousand corpses lie.

Mother whose heart hung humble as a button
On the bright splendid shroud of your son,
Do not weep.
War is kind.

ONO NO YOSHIKI

Kokim Shū

[translated from the Japanese by Arthur Waley]

My love
Is like the grasses
Hidden in the deep mountain:
Though its abundance increases,
There is none that knows.

Full Fathom Five

William Shakespeare

Full fathom five thy father lies;
Of his bones are coral made;
Those are pearls that were his eyes;
Nothing of him that doth fade,
But doth suffer a sea-change
Into something rich and strange.
Sea nymphs hourly ring his knell:
   Ding-dong!
 Hark! now I hear them —
   Ding-dong, bell.

If the Owl
Calls Again

John Haines

at dusk
from the island in the river,
and it's not too cold,

I'll wait for the moon
to rise,
then take wing and glide
to meet him.

We will not speak,
but hooded against the frost
soar above
the alder flats, searching
with tawny eyes.

And then we'll sit
in the shadowy spruce and
pick the bones
of careless mice,

while the long moon drifts
toward Asia
and the river mutters
in its icy bed.

And when morning climbs
the limbs
we'll part without a sound,

fulfilled, floating
homeward as
the cold world awakens.

LONG HAIR

Gary Snyder

HUNTING season:

Once every year, the Deer catch human beings. They do various things which irresistibly draw men near them; each one selects a certain man. The Deer shoots the man, who is then compelled to skin it and carry its meat home and eat it. Then the Deer is inside the man. He waits and hides in there, but the man doesn't know it. When enough Deer have occupied enough men, they will strike all at once. The men who don't have Deer in them will also be taken by surprise, and everything will change some. This is called "takeover from inside."

Deer trails:

Deer trails run on the side hills
  cross county access roads,
  dirt ruts to bone-white
  board-house ranches,
  tumbled down.

Waist-high through manzanita,
Through sticky, prickly, crackling
  gold dry summer grass.

Deer trails lead to water,
Lead slantwise all ways
Narrowing down to one best path—
And split—
And fade away to nowhere.

Deer trails slide under freeways,
  slip into cities,
  swing back and forth in crops and orchards
  run up the sides of schools!

Deer spoor, and crisscross dusty trace
Is in my house and kicks across my books

& deer bound through my hair.

The White Horse

D.H. Lawrence

The youth
walks up to the white horse
to put its halter on
and the horse looks at him
in silence.

They are so silent
They are in another world.

The Hydrogen Dog and the Cobalt Cat

Frederick Winsor

The Hydrogen Dog and the Cobalt Cat
Side by side in the Armory sat.
Nobody thought about fusion or fission,
Everyone spoke of their peacetime mission,
   Till somebody came and opened the door.
There they were, in a neutron fog.
The Codrogen Cat and the Hybalt Dog;
   They mushroomed up with a terrible roar —
And Nobody Never was there — nomore.

Tonight at Noon

Adrian Henri

Tonight at noon
Supermarkets will advertise 3d EXTRA on everything
Tonight at noon
Children from happy families will be sent to live in a home
Elephants will tell each other human jokes
America will declare peace on Russia
World War I generals will sell poppies in the streets on November 11th
The first daffodils of autumn will appear
When the leaves fall upwards to the trees

Tonight at noon
Pigeons will hunt cats through city backyards
Hitler will tell us to fight on the beaches and on the landing fields
A tunnel full of water will be built under Liverpool
Pigs will be sighted flying in formation over Woolton
and Nelson will not only get his eye back but his arm as well
White Americans will demonstrate for equal rights
in front of the Black House
and the Monster has just created Dr Frankenstein

Girls in bikinis are moonbathing
Folksongs are being sung by real folk
Art galleries are closed to people over 21
Poets get their poems in the Top 20
Politicians are elected to insane asylums
There's jobs for everyone and nobody wants them
In back alleys everywhere teenage lovers are kissing
in broad daylight
In forgotten graveyards everywhere the dead will quietly
bury the living
and
You will tell me you love me
Tonight at noon

SELF-PITY

D.H. Lawrence

I never saw a wild thing
sorry for itself.
A small bird will drop frozen dead from a bough
without ever having felt sorry for itself.

Hearing the Wind at Night

May Swenson

I heard the wind coming,
transferred from tree to tree.
I heard the leaves
swish, wishing to be free

to come with the wind, yet wanting to stay
with the boughs like sleeves.
The wind was a green ghost.
Possessed of tearing breath

the body of each tree
whined, a whipping post,
then straightened and resumed
its vegetable oath.

I heard the wind going,
and it went wild.
Somewhere the forest threw itself
into tantrum like a child.

I heard the trees tossing
in punishment or grief,
then sighing, and soughing,
soothing themselves to sleep.

Riot Rimes U.S.A.

Raymond R. Patterson

1

We are the same in our despair
Who now disturb your peace with riot —
The dark oppressed of yesteryear
Who swallowed grief and bled in quiet.

2

I felt this itching all over
My skin
So I smashed that plate-glass window in,
And all that fancy furniture
And easy credit plans
Were right there in my hands —
All the things I'd been needing
And I didn't know my hands were bleeding.

3

The cop said I threw the brick
Then he took his great big stick
And hit me six times quick.
But I didn't, but I might
If my poor head ever gets right.

4

These streets ain't paved with gold
Like we've been told.
But, my, that broken glass did glitter
Like diamonds in the trash and litter.

5

Willie Lee
Finally got
His color TV.
Then he got shot.

In the desert

Stephen Crane

In the desert
I saw a creature, naked, bestial,
Who, squatting upon the ground,
Held his heart in his hands,
And ate of it.
I said, "Is it good, friend?"
"It is bitter-bitter," he answered;
"But I like it
Because it is bitter,
And because it is my heart."

The Gray Squirrel

Humbert Wolfe

Like a small gray
coffeepot
sits the squirrel.
He is not

all he should be,
kills by dozens
trees, and eats
his red-brown cousins.

The keeper, on the
other hand,
who shot him, is
a Christian, and

loves his enemies,
which shows
the squirrel was not
one of those.

Counting the Mad

Donald Justice

This one was put in a jacket,
This one was sent home,
This one was given bread and meat
But would eat none,
And this one cried No No No No
All day long.

This one looked at the window
As though it were a wall,
This one saw things that were not there,
This one things that were,
And this one cried No No No No
All day long.

This one thought himself a bird,
This one a dog,
And this one thought himself a man,
An ordinary man,
And cried and cried No No No No
All day long.

All in green went my love riding

e.e. cummings

All in green went my love riding
on a great horse of gold
into the silver dawn.

four lean hounds crouched low and smiling
the merry deer ran before.

Fleeter be they than dappled dreams
the swift sweet deer
the red rare deer.

Four red roebuck at a white water
the cruel bugle sang before.

Horn at hip went my love riding
riding the echo down
into the silver dawn.

four lean hounds crouched low and smiling
the level meadows ran before.

Softer be they than slippered sleep
the lean lithe deer
the fleet flown deer.

Four fleet does at a gold valley
the famished arrow sang before.

Bow at belt went my love riding
riding the mountain down
into the silver dawn.

four lean hounds crouched low and smiling
the sheer peaks ran before.

Paler be they than daunting death
the sleek slim deer
the tall tense deer.

Four tall stags at a green mountain
the lucky hunter sang before.

All in green went my love riding
on a great horse of gold
into the silver dawn.

four lean hounds crouched low and smiling
my heart fell dead before.

The Look

Sara Teasdale

Strephon kissed me in the spring,
  Robin in the fall,
But Colin only looked at me
  And never kissed at all.

Strephon's kiss was lost in jest,
  Robin's lost in play,
But the kiss in Colin's eyes
  Haunts me night and day.

I Will Give My Love an Apple

(anonymous)

I will give my love an apple without e'er a core,
I will give my love a house without e'er a door,
I will give my love a palace wherein she may be,
And she may unlock it without any key.

My head is the apple without e'er a core,
My mind is the house without e'er a door,
My heart is the palace wherein she may be,
And she may unlock it without any key.

Love

B. P. Nichol

EEKA, NEEKA

Walter de la Mare

Eeka, Neeka, Leeka, Lee —
Here's a lock without a key;
Bring a lantern, bring a candle,
Here's a door without a handle;
Shine, shine, you old thief Moon,
Here's a door without a room;
Not a whisper, moth or mouse,
Key — lock — door — room: where's the house?

Say nothing, creep away,
And live to knock another day!

THE HARE

Walter de la Mare

In the black furrow of a field
I saw an old witch-hare this night;
And she cocked a lissome ear,
And she eyed the moon so bright,
And she nibbled of the green;
And I whispered "Whsst! witch-hare,"
Away like a ghostie o'er the field
She fled, and left the moonlight there.

The Beautiful Tiger

Keith Gunderson

parting of grasses – beautiful tiger – flutter of fern – beautiful tiger – moving through green through green his orange through green – beautiful tiger – moving through green through green through green his orange – beautiful tiger – under the vine – beautiful tiger – over the brush – beautiful tiger – branches of brown and brown his orange by branches of brown – beautiful tiger – branches of brown and brown by branches of brown his orange – beautiful tiger – loping a stream – beautiful tiger – gliding through tangle – beautiful tiger – gliding through tangle his orange through tangle his tangle through orange his orange through tangle – beautiful tiger – path to a clearing – beautiful tiger – whispering feet – beautiful tiger – disguised as an edge – beautiful tiger – looking:

OWL

George MacBeth

is my favourite. Who flies
like a nothing through the night,
who-whoing. Is a feather
duster in leafy corners ring-a-rosy-ing
boles of mice. Twice

you hear him call. Who
is he looking for? You hear
him hovering over the floor
of the wood. O would you be gold
rings in the driving skull

if you could? Hooded and
vulnerable by the winter suns
owl looks. Is the grain of bark
in the dark. Round beaks are at
work in the pellety nest,

resting. Owl is an eye
in the barn. For a hole
in the trunk owl's blood
is to blame. Black talons in the
petrified fur! Cold walnut hands

on the case of the brain! In the reign
of the chicken owl comes like
a god. Is a goad in
the rain to the pink eyes,
dripping. For a meal in the day

flew, killed, on the moor. Six
mouths are the seed of his
arc in the season. Torn meat
from the sky. Owl lives
by the claws of his brain. On the branch

in the sever of the hand's
twigs owl is a backward look.
Flown wind in the skin. Fine
rain in the bones. Owl breaks
like the day. Am an owl, am an owl.

Ma Rainey was a famous singer of the
blues in the 1920s.

A Dance for Ma Rainey

Al Young

I'm going to be just like you, Ma
Rainey this monday morning
clouds puffing up out of my head
like those balloons
that float above the faces of white people
in the funnypapers

I'm going to hover in the corners
of the world, Ma
& sing from the bottom of hell
up to the tops of high heaven
& send out scratchless waves of yellow
& brown & that basic black honey
misery

I'm going to cry so sweet
& so low
& so dangerous
Ma,
that the message is going to reach you
back in 1922

where you shimmer
snaggle-toothed
perfumed &
powdered
in your bauble beads
hair pressed & tied back
throbbing with that sick pain
I know
& hide so well
that pain that blues
jives the world with
aching to be heard
that downness
that bottomlessness
first felt by some stolen delta nigger
swamped under with redblooded american agony;
reduced to the sheer crap
of existence
that bred
& battered us all,
Ma,
the beautiful people
our beautiful people
our beautiful brave black people
who no longer need to jazz
or sing to themselves in murderous vibrations
or play the veins of their strong tender arms
with needles
to prove that we're still here.

Bottomland

John Caddy

In a sullen backwater
of the bottomland
black sawed-off pilings
curve out on the water in a long sweep
and abruptly stop.
Debris from the flood, most
the dead river brown,
clots the slow surface,
turning in yellow scum
broken by patches of oil.

I see a dead carp, its up eye
picked out, leaving only
the white socket.
The carp gently
lips the wet side of the near piling,
mouthing brown flood leavings, moss,
and the rotting wood.

A pair of canvas gloves
soaked black with oil
lie on the coarse top of this pile
lined up as though wrists jutted from them,
both on their backs, with the fingers
full and curled as if filled with drowned flesh,
distended fingers and thumbs
gesturing, palms up.

Where I am standing the wind twitches me
the smell of the carp of the yellow algae
of the clots slowly turning.
The hairs rise on my arms,
I take part in these
dumb supplicating hands,
and below them,
the blind carp, mouthing.

my sweet old etcetera

e.e. cummings

my sweet old etcetera
aunt lucy during the recent

war could and what
is more did tell you just
what everybody was fighting

for,
my sister

isabel created hundreds
(and
hundreds) of socks not to
mention shirts fleaproof earwarmers

etcetera wristers etcetera, my
mother hoped that

i would die etcetera
bravely of course my father used
to become hoarse talking about how it was
a privilege and if only he
could meanwhile my

self etcetera lay quietly
in the deep mud et

cetera
(dreaming,
et

      cetera, of
Your smile
eyes knees and of your Etcetera)

And what shoulder, and what art,
Could twist the sinews of thy heart?
And when thy heart began to beat,
What dread hand and what dread feet?

What the hammer? what the chain?
In what furnace was thy brain?
What the anvil? what dread grasp
Dare its deadly terrors clasp?

When the stars threw down their spears,
And water'd heaven with their tears,
Did He smile his work to see?
Did He who made the lamb make thee?

Tiger! Tiger! burning bright
In the forests of the night,
What immortal hand or eye
Dare frame thy fearful symmetry?

THE TIGER

William Blake

Tiger! Tiger! burning bright
In the forests of the night,
What immortal hand or eye
Could frame thy fearful symmetry?

In what distant deeps or skies
Burnt the fire of thine eyes?
On what wings dare he aspire?
What the hand dare seize the fire?

The Wind Shrieked Loud

Elizabeth Coatsworth

What I know
no one dreams.
The wind that night
covered all screams,
the moon preferred
to mantle her head,
the cook and butler
were long in bed.

I could not sleep
the wind was so loud,
a white eye glared
from a tattered cloud,
I could not sleep,
I went down the hall,
I never moved,
I saw it all.

No one shall ever
know what took place.
The moon held a darkness
over her face,
the wind shrieked loud
like a passing spirit,
I shall say nothing:
I inherit.

ME, COLORED
(from the story "Tell Freedom")

Peter Abrahams

Aunt Liza.
Yes?
What am I?
What are you talking about?
I met a boy at the river.
He said he was Zulu.
   She laughed.
You are Colored.
There are three kinds of people:
White people, Colored people,
and Black people.
The White people come first,
then the Colored people,
then the Black people.
Why?
Because it is so.

Next day when I met Joseph,
I smacked my chest and said:
   Me, Colored!
He clapped his hands and laughed.

Joseph and I spent most
of the long summer afternoons together.
He learnt some Afrikaans from me.
I learnt some Zulu from him.
Our days were full.
There was the river to explore.
There were my swimming lessons.
I learnt to fight with sticks;
to weave a green hat
of young willow wands and leaves;
to catch frogs and tadpoles
with my hands;
to set a trap for the *springhaas;*
to make the sounds of the river birds.
There was the hot sun to comfort us.
There was the green grass to dry our bodies.
There was the soft clay with which to build.
There was the fine sand with which to fight.
There were our giant grasshoppers to race.
There were the locust swarms
when the skies turned black
and we caught them by the hundreds.

There was the rare taste of crisp,
brown-baked, salted locusts.
There was the voice of the wind in the willows.
There was the voice of the heavens
in the thunder storms.
There were the voices of two children
in laughter, ours.
There were Joseph's tales of black kings
who lived in days before the white man.

At home, I said:
Aunt Liza.
Yes?
Did we have Colored kings before the white man?
No.
Then where did we come from?
Joseph and his mother come from the
black kings who were before the white man.

Laughing and ruffling my head, she said:
You talk too much. Go'n wash up.

A Date with M.G.M

Jo Cripps
(age 14)

The lion roars
And instantly you lunge at me,
Your padded fingers
Grabbing
The folded hands in my lap,
Your bicycle-pump breathing
A heavy blue
In my hair,
As the starlet sings on . . .

Your potato-skin arm
Weights my shoulder
While your hairy knuckles
Stroke my bare arm,
And only the stainless steel
Of your watchband
On my skin
Provides cold relief
From the sticky vapor
Of your presence
As the starlet sings on . . .

going uptown to visit miriam

Victor Hernandez Cruz

on the train
old ladies playing football
going for empty seats

very funny persons

the train riders
            are silly people
            i am a train rider

but no one knows where i am
going to take this train

to take this train
to take this train

the ladies   read popular
paperbacks   because they
are popular   they get off
at 42 to change for the
westside line   or off
59 for the department store

the train pulls in & out
the white walls   darkness   white walls   darkness

ladies looking up   i
wonder where they going
the dentist   pick up

husband pick up wife
pick up kids
pick up ? grass?
to library   to museum
to laundromat   to school

but no one knows where I am
going to take this train

to take this train

to visit miriam
to visit miriam

& to kiss her
on the cheek
& hope i don't
see sonia on the
street

But no one knows where i'm taking
this train
        taking this train
        to visit miriam.

It Is an Outfielder

Ron Loewinsohn

The playground is so filled with kids
that their games overlap, the
outfielders of one game
standing on the basepaths of the opposite
diamond; running around in between.
A fat girl out in left field
is standing with her arms folded
talking to a boy while she (nervously)
adjusts her glasses.
Suddenly she turns, unfolds her arms
& catches a fly ball for the 3rd out.

SADNESS

Barbara Snead
(age 15)

The reindeer is sad
because in the summertime
people kill them
and in the winter
they not be out much.
He looks sad
his ears look like trees without leaves
nobody else have ears like them.

The beach is cold
there is no soul
because no one is out there
people they be cold
sometimes part of the ocean be frozen
sometimes some of the fishes die
because there is no air

is there really mermaids?
in the wintertime they be sad
they have nowhere to get comfort
do they die?

when it dies it floats.
They should be buried
but there is no one to bury them
in the sea.
They need air just like we do
if they are buried in the world
like we do
they would smell bad.

The Flower-Fed Buffaloes

Vachel Lindsay

The flower-fed buffaloes of the spring
In the days of long ago,
Ranged where the locomotives sing
And the prairie flowers lie low:
The tossing, blooming, perfumed grass
Is swept away by wheat,
Wheels and wheels and wheels spin by
In the spring that still is sweet.
But the flower-fed buffaloes of the spring
Left us long ago.
They gore no more, they bellow no more,
They trundle around the hills no more: —
With the Blackfeet lying low,
With the Pawnees lying low.

Peruvian
Dance
Song

Wake up, woman,
Rise up, woman,
In the middle of the street
A dog howls.

May the death arrive,
May the dance arrive,

Comes the dance
You must dance,
Comes the death
You can't help it!

Ah! what a chill,
Ah! what a wind. . . .

Grandfather Poem

Jo Cripps (age 14)

Your dry lips
Once
Shouting goddam you get out of my garden
Are silent
Pulled taut over stale teeth.

Brown hands that dropped stiff rabbits
Into plastic garbage bags
Became fragile and shaking,
Covered with cellophane skin
Of an Oriental yellow.

Your eyes did not change.
Disease did not close them
Or screen their laser rays.

Only now
As you lie in your oak chest
Like a geranium in a window box
Has your stare stopped burning
My eyes.

Neither Out Far
Nor In Deep

Robert Frost

The people along the sand
All turn and look one way.
They turn their back on the land.
They look at the sea all day.

As long as it takes to pass
A ship keeps raising its hull;
The wetter ground like glass
Reflects a standing gull.

The land may vary more;
But wherever the truth may be —
The water comes ashore,
And the people look at the sea.

They cannot look out far.
They cannot look in deep.
But when was that ever a bar
To any watch they keep?

Swift Things
Are Beautiful

Elizabeth Coatsworth

Swift things are beautiful:
Swallows and deer,
And lightning that falls
Bright-veined and clear,
Rivers and meteors,
Wind in the wheat,
The strong-withered horse,
The runner's sure feet.

And slow things are beautiful:
The closing of day,
The pause of the wave
That curves downward to spray,
The ember that crumbles,
The opening flower,
And the ox that moves on
In the quiet of power.

The Base Stealer

Robert Francis

Poised between going on and back, pulled
Both ways taut like a tightrope-walker,
Fingertips pointing the opposites,
Now bouncing tiptoe like a dropped ball
Or a kid skipping rope, come on, come on,
Running a scattering of steps sidewise,
How he teeters, skitters, tingles, teases,
Taunts them, hovers like an ecstatic bird,
He's only flirting, crowd him, crowd him,
Delicate, delicate, delicate, delicate — now!

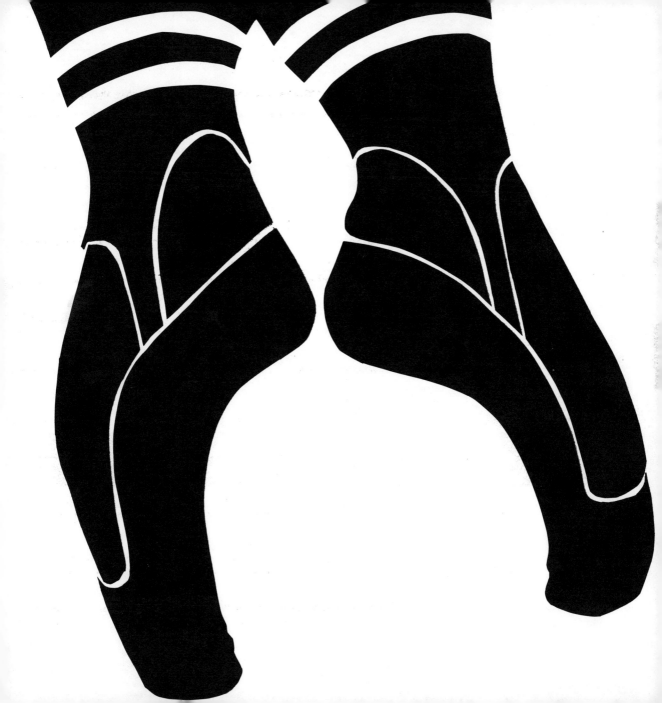

Acknowledgments (continued):

"Sea Lullaby," copyright 1921 by Alfred A. Knopf, Inc. and renewed 1949 by William Rose Benet. Reprinted from *Collected Poems* by Elinor Wylie, by permission of Alfred A. Knopf, Inc.

"Picture #16," from *Pictures of the Gone World.* Copyright © 1955 by Lawrence Ferlinghetti. Reprinted by permission of City Lights Books.

"The Sorrow of Kodio," copyright © 1959 by The Atlantic Monthly Company, Boston, Mass. Reprinted with permission.

"Ghost Dance Songs," from "The Ghost-Dance Religion" by James Mooney in the *14th Annual Report of the Bureau of American Ethnology, 1892–93. Part 2* by J. W. Powell.

"Feeding the Lions" by Norman Jordan, from *The New Black Poetry,* edited by Clarence Major, copyright © 1969 by International Publishers Co., Inc.

"three days/out of Franklin" and "going uptown to visit miriam," from *Snaps* by Victor Hernandez Cruz. Copyright © 1968, 1969 by Victor Hernandez Cruz. Reprinted by permission of Random House, Inc.

"Snake," from *Collected Poems of Theodore Roethke,* copyright © 1953, 1955 by Theodore Roethke. Reprinted by permission of Doubleday & Company, Inc.

"Complete Destruction," from *Collected Earlier Poems,* copyright 1938 by William Carlos Williams. Reprinted by permission of New Directions Publishing Corporation.

"Epitaph," from *Selected Poems* by Malcolm Lowry. Copyright © 1962 by Margerie Lowry. Reprinted by permission of City Lights Books.

"Suicide's Note," copyright 1926 by Alfred A. Knopf, Inc. and renewed 1954 by Langston Hughes. Reprinted from *Selected Poems* by Langston Hughes, by permission of Alfred A. Knopf, Inc.

"That Dark Other Mountain," reprinted by permission of Robert Francis and the University of Massachusetts Press from *Come Out Into the Sun: Poems New and Selected.*

"A Sound from the Earth," from *Allegiances* by William Stafford. Copyright © 1967 by William Stafford. Used by permission of Harper & Row, Publishers, Inc.

"Concrete Trap" by Elizabeth Coatsworth, copyright 1943 by The Saturday Review Associates, Inc.; renewed 1970 by Saturday Review, Inc. Reprinted by permission of the author and *Saturday Review.*

"Invocation," reprinted by permission of the author, Helene Johnson.

"Therzacat Boogie," by Keith Gunderson, reprinted from *The Massachusetts Review,* copyright © 1963 by The Massachusetts Review, Inc.

"Christmas Morning I," copyright © 1968 by Carole Freeman. Reprinted from *Black Fire* edited by Larry Neal and LeRoi Jones, William Morrow & Co., Inc. Used with permission of the author and the Ronald Hobbs Literary Agency.

"Night Clouds," from *The Complete Poetical Works of Amy Lowell,* published by Houghton Mifflin Company.

"Black Warrior," copyright © 1968 by Norman Jordan. Reprinted from *Black Fire,* edited by Larry Neal and LeRoi Jones, William Morrow & Co., Inc. Used with permission of the author and the Ronald Hobbs Literary Agency.

"The Naming of Cats," reprinted by permission of Faber & Faber Ltd. from *Old Possum's Book of Practical Cats* by T. S. Eliot.

"400-Meter Freestyle," from *Halfway* by Maxine W. Kumin. Copyright © 1957, 1958, 1959, 1960, 1961 by Maxine W. Kumin. Reprinted by permission of Holt, Rinehart and Winston, Inc.

"Racoon," from *Collected Shorter Poems* by Kenneth Rexroth. Copyright © 1956 by New Directions Publishing Corporation. Reprinted by permission of New Directions Publishing Corporation.

"Rest Stop," reprinted from *Medical and Other Poems* by Donald Jones, by permission of University of Nebraska Press. Copyright © 1966.

Next, see "Cinquains and Turn-Around Poems," "Contrast Poems," "Be a Song Writer," and "Comparison Poems" in MAKING THINGS UP; "Memories, Memories," "Feeling Poems," and "Moods" in PEOPLE; "Move to a Story," "Work Up a Reading," and "Language Moves" in ACTING OUT; and "What's Coming Up?" in WHAT DO YOU THINK?

Poems on circled pages have been recorded. Look for them under *Lyric Poetry* in the LISTENING LIBRARY.

Illustrated by Gary Fugiwara.

Photographs by George Krause (pp. 17, 96), Robert Kaufman, courtesy of Stock, Boston (p. 53), George Gardner (p. 72), and Ira Gavrin (p. 130).